Physics CE/KS3
Topic Booklet

Energy Resources

- Read, engage and learn!
- Full colour, illustrated Topic Booklet.
- Glossary, Memory Map, Active Learning Game & Flashcards.
- Ideal for ISEB 13+ Common Entrance and KS3 pupils.

This Oaka™ Books Topic Booklet goes hand in hand with the Active Learning Pack on this topic. The pack includes a Write Your Own Notes Booklet, an Active Learning Game and Question & Answer Flashcards.

Fresh Focus on Learning

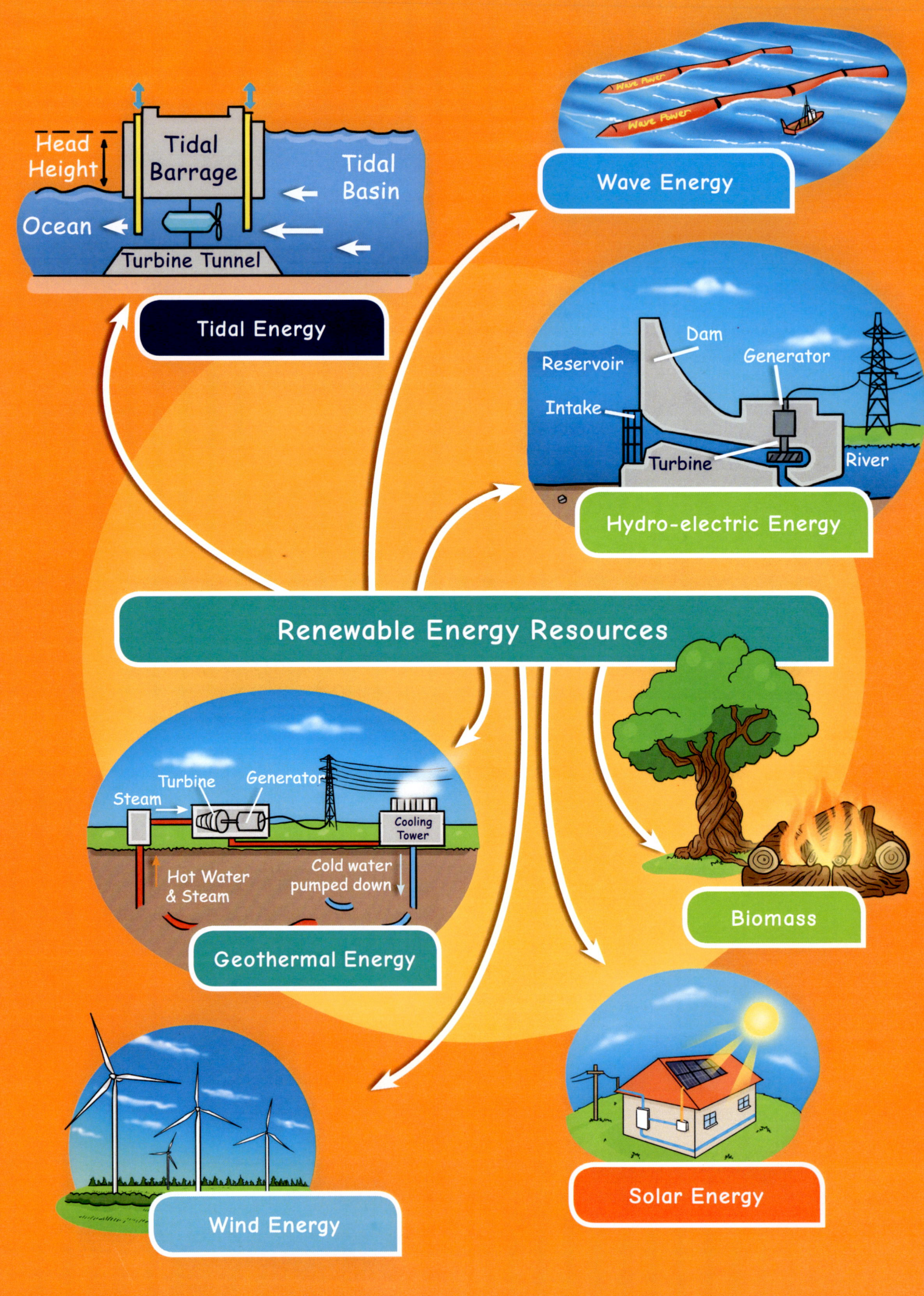

Energy Resources Glossary

 **Biomass:** Renewable energy made from plant waste.

 **Fossil:** The remains of things that lived millions of years ago.

 **Bunsen:** A burner using natural gas. Used in laboratories.

 **Generator:** Transforms kinetic (movement) energy into electricity.

 **Burn:** This means to combine with oxygen.

 **Geothermal:** Energy source from underground.

 **Coal:** Solid fuel made over millions of years ago from dead plants.

 **Hydro:** Usually refers to electric power from water held behind a dam.

Save It! **Conservation:** Keeping the total amount of energy or substances the same.

 **Kinetic Energy:** Movement energy.

 **DC/AC:** Direct Current/ Alternating Current.

 **Methane:** Bunsen burner fuel. Comes from deep underground.

 **Electrical:** The most useful form of energy.

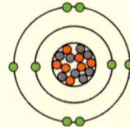 **Nuclear:** Energy generated from atoms.

 **Energy:** 6 forms are light, sound, thermal, kinetic, electrical and chemical.

 **Oil:** Liquid fuel formed over millions of years from dead sea creatures.

 **Flammable:** Can catch light.

Oxygen: Gas needed to let fuel burn.

Energy Resources Glossary

 **Photosynthesis:** Process by which green plants use sunlight to make food.

 **Solar:** Energy from the sun.

 **Photovoltaic Cell:** Making electricity by turning light into current (DC).

 **Sedimentary Rock:** Rocks formed under the sea millions of years ago.

 **Plutonium:** Fuel used in nuclear power stations.

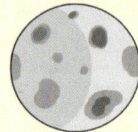 **Tidal:** The pull due to the Moon's gravitational attraction to the Earth.

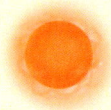 **Radiation:** How energy from the Sun comes to Earth.

 **Transfer:** When energy stored in one form is changed to a different form.

 **Radio Active:** A powerful and dangerous form of nuclear energy.

 **Turbine:** Machine for making power. It spins as a liquid or gas flows through it.

 **Renewable Energy:** Energy that will not run out e.g. solar and wind. (Can be replenished within a lifetime)

 **Uranium:** Fuel for nuclear power stations.

 **Resource:** Where the energy or mineral comes from.

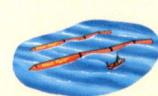 **Wave:** The crests and troughs on a substance when it moves from one place to another.

Law of Conservation Energy

Energy is neither created nor destroyed.
It is just transferred from one form to another.

Energy

1   Fuels

- Fuels are materials that we **burn** to release **energy**.

- Fuels give us **light**, **thermal (heat)** and **kinetic** (movement) **energy**.

Kinetic Energy

Light Energy

Thermal Energy

2   Useful Energy

- But when we use energy (doing work) the energy is always spread out. But is **not** destroyed.

- This makes some of it less useful.

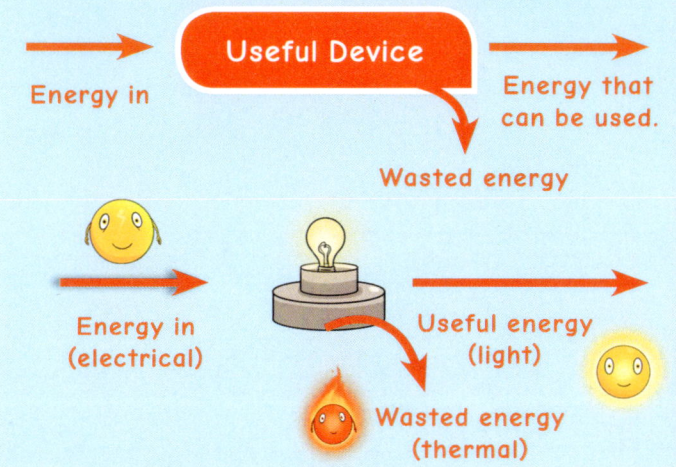

3   Energy is Transferred in Many Ways

- Plants trap **energy**, from the sun when they make their food by photosynthesis.

- Animals eat plants and use some of the **energy** trapped in the plant.

- The **energy** trapped in trees is also released when we **burn** them.

Chemical Energy

4 — Chemical Energy in Fuel

- The **energy** trapped in fuels, like **coal**, is called **chemical energy**.

- When we **burn** fuels the **chemical energy** is **converted into thermal** and **light** energy.

Coal   Contains   Chemical Energy

5 — Chemical Energy in Food

- Food is also a fuel that contains **chemical energy**.

- We eat food. The **chemical energy** in the food is **converted into thermal** and **kinetic energy**.

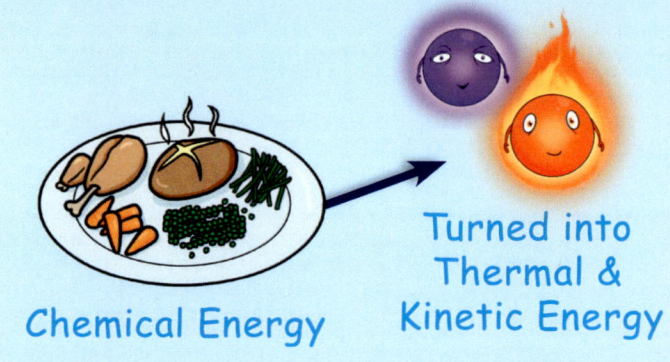

Chemical Energy   Turned into Thermal & Kinetic Energy

6 — Chemical Energy in a Battery

- Batteries also contain **chemical energy**.

- The **chemical energy** in a battery may be **converted into electrical**, **thermal (heat)**, **light**, **kinetic** or **sound energy**.

Batteries   contain   Chemical Energy

7 — Chemical Energy Transfer

- A torch **transfers**... chemical energy → light & thermal energy.

electrical

- A radio **transfers**... chemical energy → sound energy.

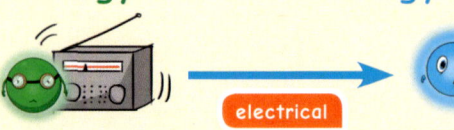

electrical

- A train set **transfers**... chemical energy → kinetic, thermal and sound energy.

electrical

Energy Resources

8   Energy Resources

- **Energy Resources** can be divided into two groups...

  1. Non-Renewable
  2. Renewable

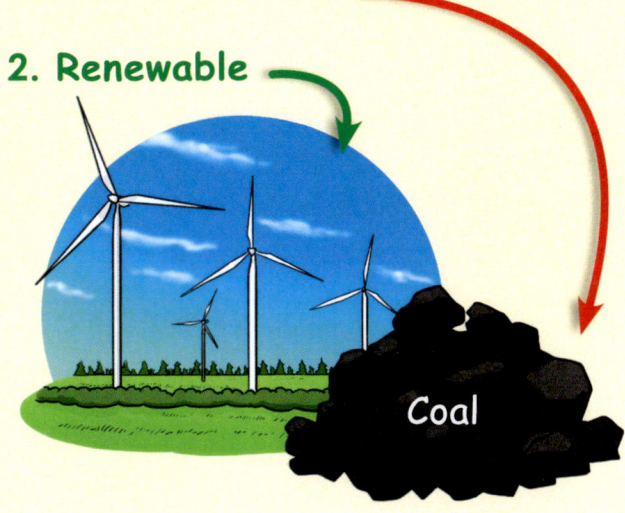

Coal

9   Non-Renewable

- **Non-renewable** energy **resources cannot** be replaced.

- **Coal, oil, natural gas** and **nuclear** are examples of **non-renewable energy resources**.

10   Fossil Fuels

- **Coal, oil** and **natural gas** are **fossil fuels**.

- They were made from the **remains of living things** that died millions of years ago.

11   Fossil Fuels

- The world will **run out** of **fossil fuels**.

- **Fossil fuels** cannot be made again. They are **non-renewable**.

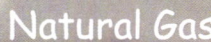
Natural Gas

Coal

Oil

Fossil Fuels

12   How is Coal Made?

- The Sun is the source of most of the Earth's energy resources.

- **Coal** is made from dead plants.

- Plants contain the **energy** from the **Sun**. This energy is trapped as they make their food by **photosynthesis**.

1. Millions of years ago, many giant plants died in swamps.

3. Heat and pressure turned the dead plants into coal.

2. The dead plants were buried by dirt.

Dead Plants

13   How is Oil Made?

- **Oil** is made from **plants and animals** that died in the **oceans**.

- The plants contain the **energy** from the **Sun**, trapped as they made their food by **photosynthesis**.

- The animals contain the **chemical energy** from the food that they have eaten.

- The plants and animals were buried by mud and sand millions of years ago.

Contains chemical energy from food.

Fossil Fuels

14   How is Natural Gas Made?

- Natural gas is made in the same way as **oil**.

- Natural gas and **oil** deposits are found **together** under the sea.

Dead organisms, plants & animals

Impermeable rocks

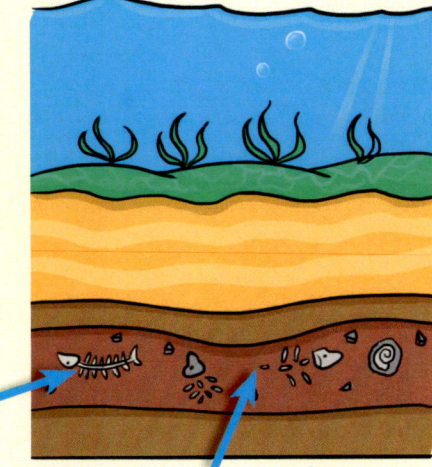
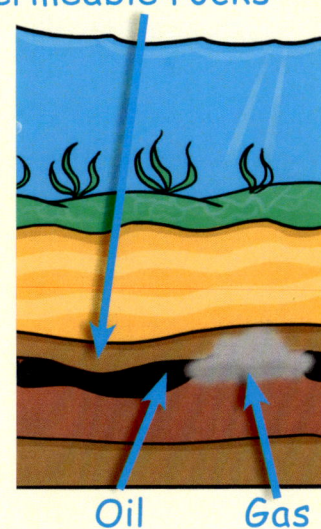

Trapped Fossils

Sedimentary rocks

Oil   Gas

15   Making Fossil Fuels

- The dead plants and animals, need to be **buried** before they can rot away.

- They have to be **squashed** under millions of tonnes of dirt, mud and sand.

16   High Pressure

- This causes **high pressure** and **temperature**.

- The dead plants and animals become **fossil fuels**.

- This takes millions of years!

- The **energy** in **fossil fuels** first came from the **Sun**!

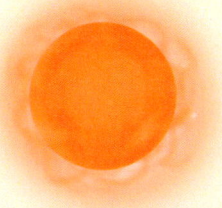

Renewable Energy

17   Renewable Energy

- **Renewable energy resources** will not run out.

- They will be renewed by the Sun's energy.

18   Saving Fossil Fuels

- We need to use more **renewable energy resources** to **save** the **fossil fuels** that we have left.

Fossil fuels will run out!

19   Biomass

- Plants are a good source of **renewable energy**.

- Plants can be grown to be used as fuels. We call this **biomass**.

20   Biofuels

- Plants, like sugar cane, can be used as a fuel for cars.

- Sugar cane is used as a **food** for **micro-organisms**. They turn the sugar cane into **alcohol**.

- The **alcohol** is used instead of **petrol**.

Renewable Energy

21 Wind Energy

- The **energy** in the wind can be used to turn big **turbines** on wind farms.

- Wind **energy** is **transferred** as **kinetic** (movement) **energy**.

- The **kinetic energy** is used to turn **generators**. They convert kinetic energy into **electrical energy**.

22 Wave Energy

- Big floats bob up and down as the waves go by.

- The **kinetic energy** of the floats is used to turn **generators**.

- They convert kinetic energy into **electrical energy**.

23 Tidal Energy

- **Tidal energy** uses the movement of water to **generate electrical energy**.

- As the **tide rises**, water is **trapped** in rivers by **tidal** barrages.

- When the **tide falls**, the water flows over the **turbines**.

- The **kinetic energy** of the water turns the **turbines**.

- The turbines are connected to **generators**. They convert kinetic energy into **electrical energy**.

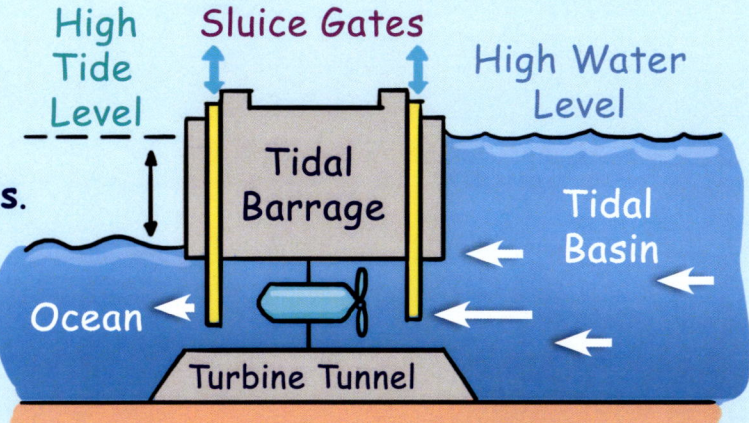

Renewable Energy

24   Hydro Electric Energy

- Hydro power uses the energy in **flowing water** to make electricity.

- Water is **trapped** up high, behind a **dam**.

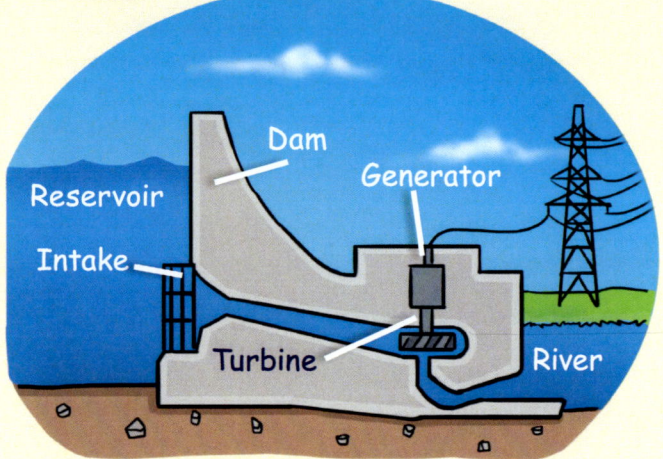

- When the water is **released**, it **flows** over turbines.

- The **kinetic energy** of the water turns the **turbines**.

- These are connected to **generators**.

- They convert kinetic energy into **electrical energy**.

- **Hydro** power produces more **energy** than any other source of **renewable energy** in the world.

25   Energy from Sunlight

- **Energy** from the Sun is called **solar power**.

- The **energy** from the Sun is **radiated** to the earth.

- Plants use **solar energy** to make food by photosythesis.

Solar Panel on roof converts sunlight into DC current

Extra electricity is saved on grid

Photovoltaic Cells convert DC to AC power

Energy Resources

26 Geothermal Energy

- **Geothermal** is using the heat from deep **underground** to heat water.

- It can be used to make **electricity** or heat homes.

- **Cold** water is pumped **down**. It **boils** and comes back up as steam.

- The **high pressure** of the steam **turns** the **turbines**.

- These are connected to **generators**.

- They convert kinetic energy into **electrical energy**.

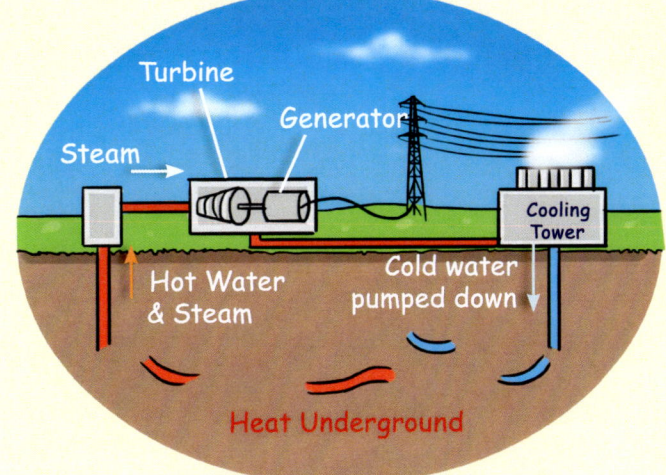

Turbine

Generator

Steam →

Cooling Tower

Hot Water & Steam

Cold water pumped down

Heat Underground

27 Non-Renewable Nuclear

- Some chemical elements, like **Plutonium** and **Uranium**, are **radioactive**.

- When their atoms **break down**, they give out **nuclear energy**.

- The nuclear energy can be used to turn water into steam to turn **turbines**.

- **Nuclear energy** produces harmful **nuclear waste** that can last for hundreds of years.

- **Nuclear** is classed as **non-renewable**.

Energy Resources

28   Using Fuels

- Fuels are **flammable**. They **burn** in **oxygen**.

- **Coal, oil, gas, biomass** and **nuclear** fuels can all be used to **generate electricity**.

- Power stations use fuels to **transfer** the chemical **energy**, trapped in fuels, into **electrical energy**.

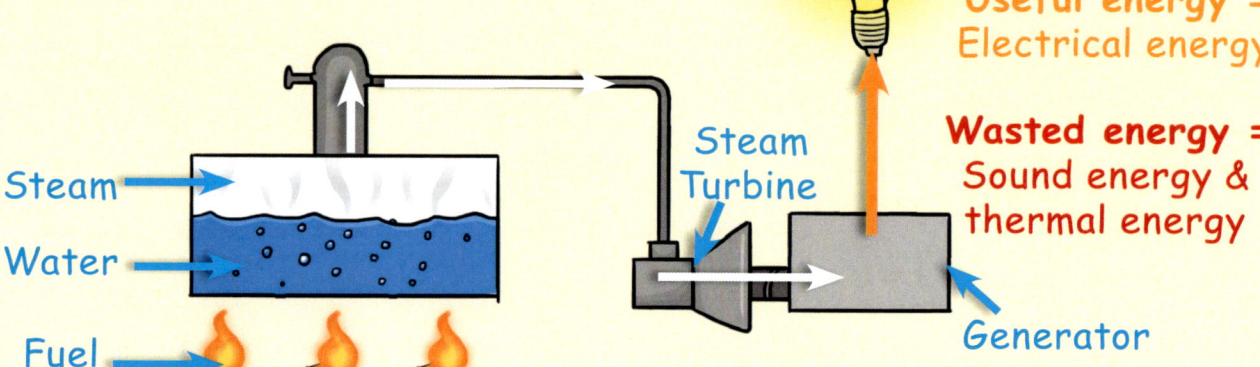

Useful energy = Electrical energy

Wasted energy = Sound energy & thermal energy

Steam

Water

Fuel

Steam Turbine

Generator

29   Joule

- The **joule** is the unit that we use to measure **energy**.

- The **joule** is a very small unit.

- It would take you 1 **joule** of **energy** to lift an apple 1 metre into the air.

30   Things to Remember About Sunlight

- The Sun is the **energy** source of nearly all the Earth's **energy resources**.

- All animals need **energy** to survive.

- Plants trap **solar energy** during photosynthesis.

- Plants are at the beginning of all food chains. Animals eat plants and we eat plants and animals.

- Food (chemical **energy**) is the **energy** source for animals.

Non-Renewable Energy

Under the Sea	Millions of years ago	On Land

Dead plants & animals in the sea.

Contain chemical energy from food.

Buried under the sea millions of years ago.

Pressure and temperature.

Made fossil fuels: Oil & Natural Gas.

Pressure

Heat

Pressure

Heat

Dead plants on the land.

Contain energy trapped during photosynthesis.

Buried under ground millions of years ago.

Pressure and temperature.

Made fossil fuel: Coal

Today

About Oaka Books

Children learn best when they are engaged...

Our aim is to help children enjoy learning by making it fun! That way they will succeed.

Following ISEB 13+ Common Entrance and National Curriculum guidelines for KS3.

Design and layout of our books follow guidelines from the British Dyslexia Association

Three Easy Steps

Read: the easy to follow bullet point Topic Booklet.

Engage: Play the Active Learning Game.

Learn: When you understand the topic, test yourself using the Write Your Own Notes Book. You can use the Topic Booklet to help if you get stuck.

One (short) Topic at a time:

For some students, a big book is a big turn off. That's why we focus on one topic at a time. Short and to the point.

Reading Age

This booklet is suitable for children with a reading age of 10 ½ years.

Topic Packs for KS1, KS2 & KS3 Include:

History
Geography
Chemistry
Biology
Physics

Please visit www.oakabooks.co.uk for more information about forthcoming titles.

© Copyright 2018 Oaka Books. All rights reserved. Written by Stuart Lawes BSc, PGCE. Illustrations by Laurence Andrew Page.

First paperback edition printed 2015 in the United Kingdom.
A catalogue record for this book is available from the British Library.

ISBN 978-1-909892-63-7
No part of this book shall be reproduced or transmitted in any form or by any means, electronic or mechanical, including photocopying, recording or by any information retrieval system without written permission of the copyright owner or a licence permitting restricted copying issued by the Copyright Licensing Agency Ltd, Saffron House, 6-10 Kirby Street, London EC1N 8TS Tel: 020 7400 3100   Fax: 020 7400 3101   Email: cla@cla.co.uk   Web: www.cla.co.uk

Designed, set and published by Oaka™ Books.

To order other titles from Oaka™ Books, please email info@oakabooks.co.uk or visit www.oakabooks.co.uk, or phone: +44 (0) 2392 221133.

Acknowledgements
Our huge thanks go to the many teachers who have been involved in the development of this series of learning guides. Special thanks to Joy Gardiner, for producing hundreds of illustrations, to Kate Doehren, for her enthusiasm and invaluable assistance to my wonderful daughter Sophie, for being the inspiration for the books and, of course, to Charlie, for believing in them.

ISBN 978-1-909892-63-7

CE/KS3
Energy
Resources

Topic Booklet

9 781909 892637

ISBN 978-1-909892-63-7   Produced in association with Kate Doehren, MA Ed, B.Ed Hons, RSA Dip, Sp LD/Dyslexia
Head of Learning Support, Hurstpierpoint College
© Copyright Oaka™ Books 2018